Sunrise, Sunset

LYRICS BY **Sheldon Harnick** ∼ MUSIC BY **Jerry Bock**

ILLUSTRATED BY **Ian Schoenherr**

HarperCollinsPublishers

For Charlotte and Sam

Is this the little girl I carried?
Is this the little boy at play?

I don't remember growing older.
When did they?

When did she get to be a beauty?
When did he grow to be so tall?

Wasn't it yesterday

when they were small?

Sunrise, sunset,
  Sunrise, sunset,
    Swiftly flow the days;

Seedlings turn overnight to sunflow'rs,

Blossoming even as we gaze.

Sunrise, sunset,
Sunrise, sunset,
Swiftly fly the years;

One season following another,

Laden with happiness and tears.

Now is the little boy a bridegroom,
Now is the little girl a bride.

Under the canopy I see them,
Side by side.

Sunrise, Sunset • Text and music © 1964, renewed 1992, by Mayerling Productions Ltd. and Jerry Bock Enterprises •
Illustrations copyright © 2005 by Ian Schoenherr • Manufactured in China. • All rights reserved. • www.harperchildrens.com
For information address HarperCollins Children's Books, a division of HarperCollins Publishers, 10 East 53rd Street, New
York, NY 10022.

Library of Congress Cataloging-in-Publication Data Harnick, Sheldon. Sunrise, sunset / lyrics by Sheldon Harnick ;
music by Jerry Bock ; illustrated by Ian Schoenherr. — 1st ed. p. cm. Summary: An illustrated version of the
well-known song about the passage of time, from the musical "Fiddler on the Roof." ISBN 978-0-06-186429-2 (sp. bdg.)
1. Children's songs, English—United States—Texts. [1. Songs.] I. Bock, Jerry. II. Schoenherr, Ian, ill. III. Title.
PZ8.3.H2183Su 2005   2004019104   782.42—dc22   CIP   [E]   AC
Typography by Martha Rago   09 10 11 12 13 SCP 10 9 8 7 6 5 4 3 2 1 ❖ First Edition

The illustrations for this book were made with colored pencil, permanent ink, and acrylic paint on Bristol board.

One season following another,
Laden with happiness and tears.

Sunrise, sunset,
Sunrise, sunset,
Swiftly fly the years;

Seedlings turn overnight to sunflow'rs,
Blossoming even as we gaze.

Sunrise, sunset,
    Sunrise, sunset,
        Swiftly flow the days;

Place the gold ring around her finger,
Share the sweet wine and break the glass;
Soon the full circle will have come to pass.